Symbols indicate the number of hazards on the page

Hari at Home
by Tristan McGee
Edited by Sarah Cheeseman
Illustrated by Nicholas Halliday

J363.
1

First Published 2009. Reprinted 2011
Copyright © 2011 Hari's World Limited
'Hari' is a registered trademark

A CIP catalogue record of this book is available from the British Library
ISBN 978-0-9559979-4-5
Printed in England

 **Mixed Sources**
Product group from well-managed
forests and other controlled sources
www.fsc.org Cert no. TT-COC-002495
© 1996 Forest Stewardship Council
FSC

CarbonNeutral® printing company

Tristan McGee

It was late one lazy Saturday morning.
Hari and Moe were relaxing in the bedroom,
and Max was still fast asleep in Hari's toy box.
A light breeze ruffled the curtains.

Suddenly, Max woke up and peered out from under the lid.
He had heard Sting the Wasp busily buzzing about as he flew
in through the open window.

Max really enjoyed chasing wasps, especially Sting!

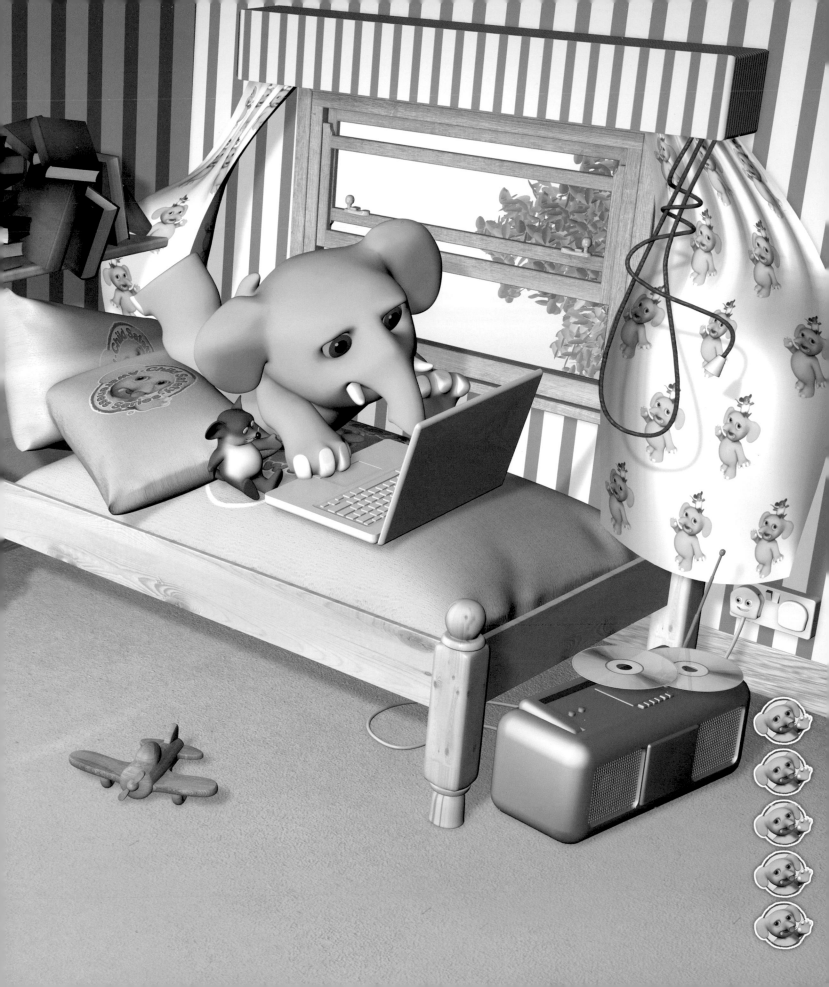

Max ran around excitedly, leaping up at Sting as he flew around the bedroom, out of the door and into the corridor.

"*Quick!*" shouted Hari, as he ran after Max.

Sting circled above Max, teasing him.

"*Try not to make him angry,*" Moe warned Max. "*He might sting you.*"

But Max wasn't listening – he was far too excited.

Oops Hari!

Max chased Sting,
Hari chased Max
and Moe chased Hari.

As Hari ran down the corridor, he tripped
over the wire from the vacuum cleaner,
sending Hari and the flowerpot

CRASHING to the floor!

"What's all this noise?" asked Mum. "What are you up to?"

"Nothing!" replied Hari.

"Good!" said Mum. "Then you can come and have your shower."

Mum put the non-slip mat in the bath. Then Hari and Moe climbed in and scrubbed themselves clean.

After their shower, Hari and Moe brushed their teeth and tusks with their favourite minty toothpaste.

Hari and Moe were still in the bathroom when Sting flew in to hide from Max.

Max sneaked around the bathroom looking for Sting.

When Max found him, he barked and barked until Sting flew out again as quickly as he could.

Max chased Sting down the corridor to the landing and collided with the stair gate, but Sting flew easily through the bars and down the stairs.

Mum opened the stair gate.

Max chased Sting,
Hari chased Max
and Moe chased Hari.

"*Don't run down the stairs!*" warned Moe.
But Max wasn't listening – he was far too excited.

Halfway down the stairs, Max missed a step and tripped.
Hari then tripped over Max
and Moe ran into Hari.

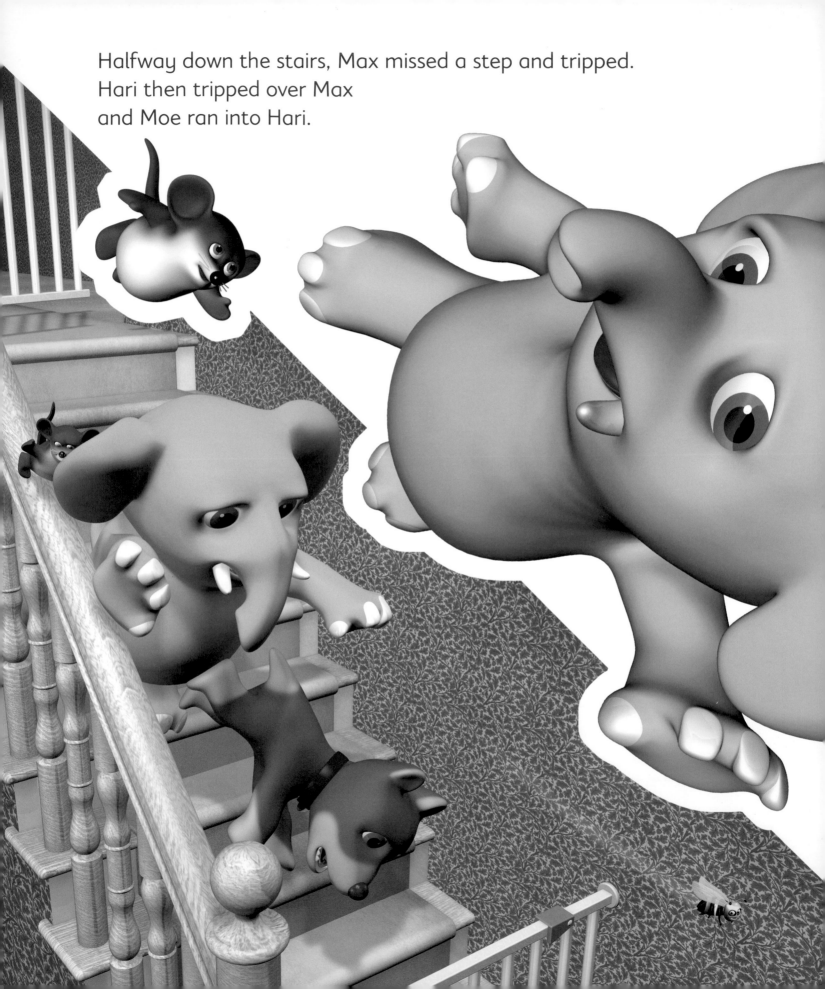

Oops Hari!

They tumbled down the stairs,
finally crashing into the stair gate at the bottom.
Max thought this was great fun, but Sting was getting angry.

There was one thing Max enjoyed even more than chasing Sting, and that was eating.

So to calm Max down, Moe gave him his favourite food.

"We should leave Max alone while he's eating," Moe said to Hari, but Hari was already busy enjoying a healthy snack.

Tired after being chased all over the house by Max, Sting flew into the kitchen quietly and found a safe place to have a rest.

While they were eating, Sting escaped through the kitchen door and into the garden.

Sting was glad Max hadn't seen him ...

... but Max was crafty and peered round the door to see Sting flying into the garage to hide...

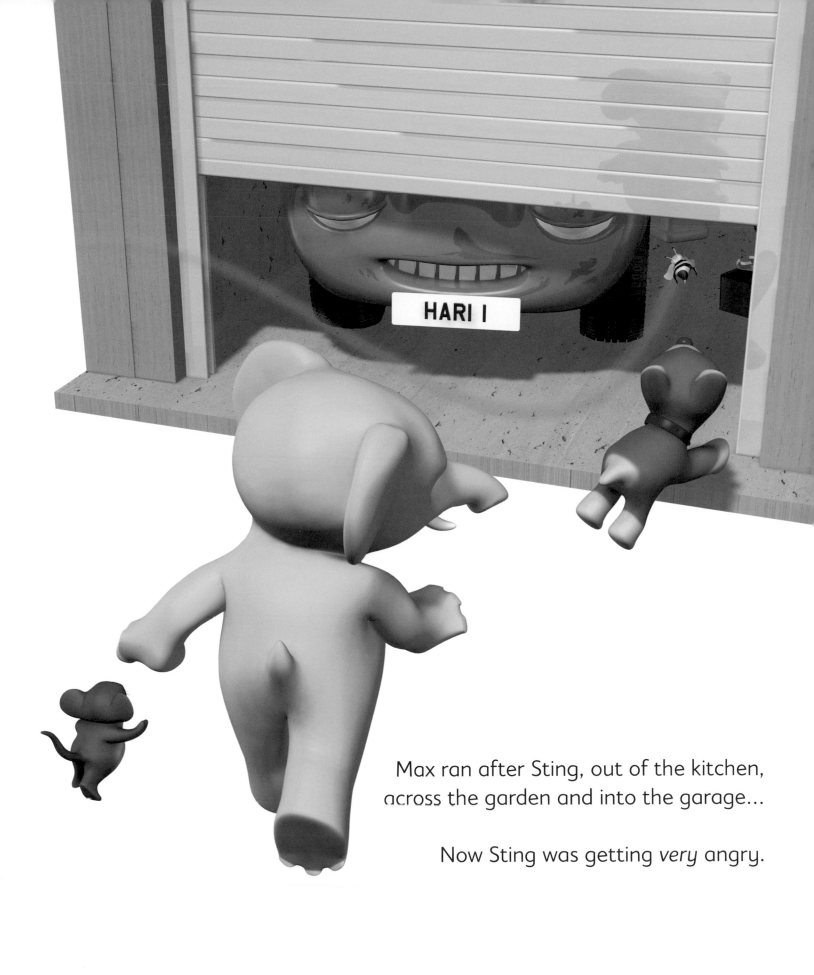

Max ran after Sting, out of the kitchen, across the garden and into the garage...

Now Sting was getting *very* angry.

"We aren't allowed in there," said Moe.

Max was far too excited, and was already sneaking into the garage to find Sting.

Sting found a place to hide and kept very quiet!

Max finally found Sting and chased him out of the garage,
down the garden and home to his tree, where he hid amongst the leaves.

Now Sting was VERY angry.

After being chased out of the bedroom,
the bathroom, the kitchen and the garage,
Sting was NOT going to be chased out of his own home.

While Max, Hari and Moe climbed the tree, Sting gathered his family.

Then each wasp chose someone to sting.

'Ouch!' cried Hari.
'Ouch!' cried Moe.
'Ouch!' cried Max.

Oops Hari! Oops Moe! Oops Max!

Max followed Moe and
Hari followed Max,
as the angry wasps
chased them all back up
the garden and into the house.

Safely back in the bedroom, Mum put ointment on their stings, and then Hari and Moe played a game on their computer.

"I'm glad Max is asleep and not causing any more trouble," said Moe.

"Yes," said Hari, "but we don't know what he's dreaming about, do we?"

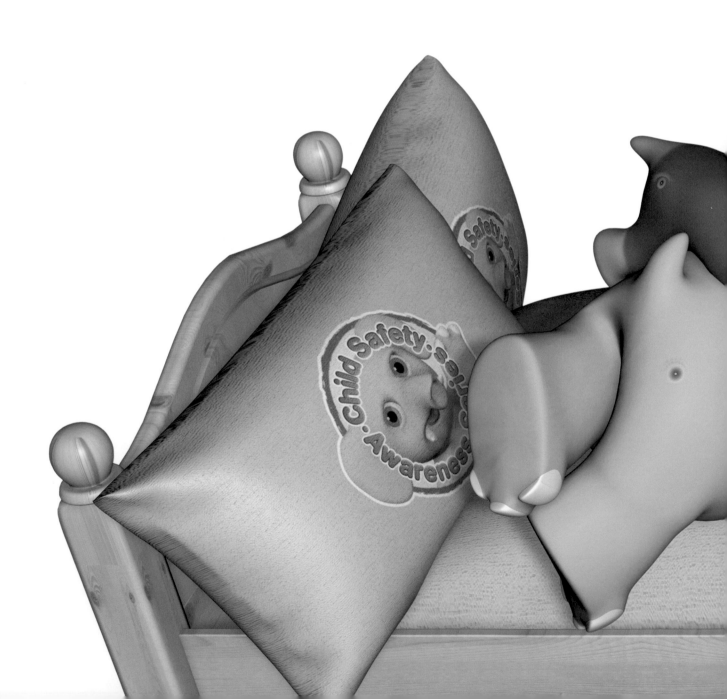

There are three books currently available
in the Oops Hari! series for you to enjoy

When Hari gets up late from his nap, he has to rush to meet his friends,
but he can't find his bicycle helmet. Moe is trying to tell him
where it is, but Hari just isn't listening!

ISBN 978-0-9559979-0-7

When Sting the Wasp flies into Hari's bedroom on a lazy Saturday morning,
Max the Dog begins a chase that leads them all over the house
and garden. Moe tries to warn Max about annoying Sting,
but Max just isn't listening!

ISBN 978-0-9559979-4-5

When Pinch the Crab is found in his little rock pool on a sunny day
at the beach, Hari and Max the Dog begin a chase that leads
them along the beach and the pier to the cliff bottom.
Moe tries to warn them about annoying Pinch,
but they just aren't listening. When Hari
and his friends go for a swim,
Pinch has other ideas!

ISBN 978-0-9559979-6-9